William Wilkie Collins (8 January 1824 – 23 September 1889) was an English novelist, playwright, and short story writer, best known for The Woman in White (1859), No Name (1862), Armadale (1866) and The Moonstone (1868). The last has been called the first modern English detective novel. Born to the family of painter William Collins in London, he grew up in Italy and France, learning French and Italian. He began work as a clerk for a tea merchant. After his first novel, Antonina, appeared in 1850, he met Charles Dickens, who became a close friend and mentor. Some of Collins's works appeared first in Dickens's journals All the Year Round and Household Words and they collaborated on drama and fiction. Collins published his best known works in the 1860s, achieving financial stability and an international following. However, he began suffering from gout. Taking opium for the pain developed into an addiction. In the 1870s and 1880s the quality of his writing declined along with his health. Collins was critical of the institution of marriage: he split his time between Caroline Graves, except for a two-year separation, and his common-law wife Martha Rudd, with whom he had three children. (Source: Wikipedia)

Literary works:
Basil (1852)
Hide and Seek (1854)
The Dead Secret (1856)
The Frozen Deep (1857)
"A House to Let" (1858)
"The Haunted House"
The Woman in White (1860)
No Name (1862)
Armadale (1866)
No Thoroughfare (1867)
The Moonstone (1868)
Man and Wife (1870)
Poor Miss Finch (1872)
The Law and the Lady (1875)
The Fallen Leaves (1879)

A Fair Penitent
Wilkie Collins

PRINCE CLASSICS

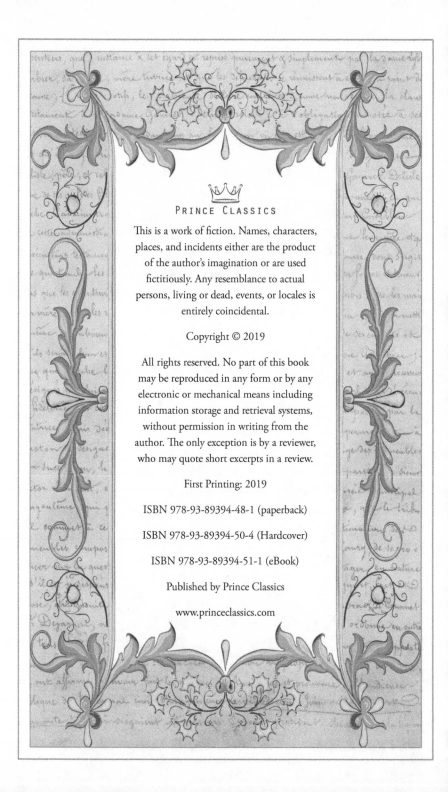

PRINCE CLASSICS

First Printing: 2019

ISBN 978-93-89394-48-1 (paperback)

ISBN 978-93-89394-50-4 (Hardcover)

ISBN 978-93-89394-51-1 (eBook)

Published by Prince Classics

www.princeclassics.com

Contents

A Fair Penitent

About "A Fair Penitent"

This story first appeared in Charles Dickens' magazine, "Household Words," volume 16, number 382, July 18, 1857. Published anonymously, as all contributions to the magazine were, it was attributed definitely to Wilkie Collins by Anne Lohrli in her analysis of the magazine's financial accounts.

A FAIR PENITENT

Charles Pineau Duclos was a French writer of biographies and novels, who lived and worked during the first half of the eighteenth century. He prospered sufficiently well, as a literary man, to be made secretary to the French Academy, and to be allowed to succeed Voltaire in the office of historiographer of France. He has left behind him, in his own country, the reputation of a lively writer of the second class, who addressed the public of his day with fair success, and who, since his death, has not troubled posterity to take any particular notice of him.

Among the papers left by Duclos, two manuscripts were found, which he probably intended to turn to some literary account. The first was a brief Memoir, written by himself, of a Frenchwoman, named Mademoiselle Gautier, who began life as an actress and who ended it as a Carmelite nun. The second manuscript was the lady's own account of the process of her conversion, and of the circumstances which attended her moral passage from the state of a sinner to the state of a saint. There are certain national peculiarities in the character of Mademoiselle Gautier and in the narrative of her conversion, which are perhaps interesting enough to be reproduced with some chance of pleasing the present day.

It appears, from the account given of her by Duclos, that Mademoiselle Gautier made her appearance on the stage of the Théâtre François in the year seventeen hundred and sixteen. She is described as a handsome woman, with a fine figure, a fresh complexion, a lively disposition, and a violent temper. Besides possessing capacity as an actress, she could write very good verses, she was clever at painting in miniature, and, most remarkable quality of all, she was possessed of prodigious muscular strength. It is recorded of Mademoiselle, that she could roll up a silver plate with her hands, and that she covered herself with distinction in a trial of strength with no less a person than the famous soldier, Marshal Saxe.

Nobody who is at all acquainted with the social history of the eighteenth century in France, need be told that Mademoiselle Gautier had a long list of lovers,—for the most part, persons of quality, marshals, counts, and so forth. The only man, however, who really attached her to him, was an actor at the Théâtre François, a famous player in his day, named Quinault Dufresne. Mademoiselle Gautier seems to have loved him with all the ardour of her naturally passionate disposition. At first, he returned her affection; but, as soon as she ventured to test the sincerity of his attachment by speaking of marriage, he cooled towards her immediately, and the connection between them was broken off. In all her former love-affairs, she had been noted for the high tone which she adopted towards her admirers, and for the despotic authority which she exercised over them even in her gayest moments. But the severance of her connection with Quinault Dufresne wounded her to her heart. She had loved the man so dearly, had made so many sacrifices for him, had counted so fondly on the devotion of her whole future life to him, that the first discovery of his coldness towards her broke her spirit at once and for ever. She fell into a condition of hopeless melancholy, looked back with remorse and horror at her past life, and abandoned the stage and the society in which she had lived, to end her days repentantly in the character of a Carmelite nun.

So far, her history is the history of hundreds of other women before her time and after it. The prominent interest of her life, for the student of human nature, lies in the story of her conversion, as told by herself. The greater part of the narrative—every page of which is more or less characteristic of the Frenchwoman of the eighteenth century—may be given, with certain suppressions and abridgments, in her own words. The reader will observe, at the outset, one curious fact. Mademoiselle Gautier does not so much as hint at the influence which the loss of her lover had in disposing her mind to reflect on serious subjects. She describes her conversion as if it had taken its rise in a sudden inspiration from Heaven. Even the name of Quinault Dufresne is not once mentioned from one end of her narrative to the other.

On the twenty-fifth of April, seventeen hundred and twenty-two (writes Mademoiselle Gautier), while I was still leading a life of pleasure—according to the pernicious ideas of pleasure which pass current in the world—I happen to awake, contrary to my usual custom, between eight and nine o'clock in the morning. I remember that it is my birthday; I ring for my people; and my maid answers the bell, alarmed by the idea that I am ill. I tell her to dress me that I may go to mass. I go to the Church of the Cordeliers, followed by my footman, and taking with me a little orphan whom I had adopted. The first part of the mass is celebrated without attracting my attention; but, at the second part the accusing voice of my conscience suddenly begins to speak. "What brings you here?" it says. "Do you come to reward God for making you the attractive person that you are, by mortally transgressing His laws every day of your life?" I hear that question, and I am unspeakably overwhelmed by it. I quit the chair on which I have hitherto been leaning carelessly, and I prostrate myself in an agony of remorse on the pavement of the church.

The mass over, I send home the footman and the orphan, remaining behind myself, plunged in inconceivable perplexity. At last I rouse myself on a sudden; I go to the sacristy; I demand a mass for my own proper advantage every day; I determine to attend it regularly; and, after three hours of agitation, I return home, resolved to enter on the path that leads to justification.

Six months passed. Every morning I went to my mass: every evening I spent in my customary dissipations.

Some of my friends indulged in considerable merriment at my expense when they found out my constant attendance at mass. Accordingly, I disguised myself as a boy, when I went to church, to escape observation. My disguise was found out, and the jokes against me were redoubled. Upon this, I began to think of the words of the Gospel, which declare the impossibility of serving two masters. I determined to abandon the service of Mammon.

The first vanity I gave up was the vanity of keeping a maid. By way of further accustoming myself to the retreat from the world which I now began to meditate, I declined all invitations to parties under the pretext of indisposition. But the nearer the Easter time approached at which I had settled in my own mind definitely to turn my back on worldly temptations and pleasures, the more violent became my internal struggles with myself. My health suffered under them to such an extent that I was troubled with perpetual attacks of retching and sickness, which, however, did not prevent me from writing my general confession, addressed to the vicar of Saint Sulpice, the parish in which I lived.

Just Heaven! what did I not suffer some days afterwards, when I united around me at dinner, for the last time, all the friends who had been dearest to me in the days of my worldly life! What words can describe the tumult of my heart when one of my guests said to me, "You are giving us too good a dinner for a Wednesday in Passion Week;" and when another answered, jestingly, "You forget that this is her farewell dinner to her friends!" I felt ready to faint while they were talking, and rose from table pretexting as an excuse, that I had a payment to make that evening, which I could not in honour defer any longer. The company rose with me, and saw me to the door. I got into my carriage, and the company returned to table. My nerves were in such a state that I shrieked at the first crack of the coachman's whip; and the company came running down again to know what was the matter. One of my servants cleverly stopped them from all hurrying out to the carriage together, by declaring that the scream proceeded from my adopted orphan. Upon this they returned quietly enough to their wine, and I drove off with my general confession to the vicar of Saint Sulpice.

My interview with the vicar lasted three hours. His joy at discovering that I was in a state of grace was extreme. My own emotions were quite indescribable. Late at night I returned to my own house, and found my guests all gone. I employed myself in writing farewell letters to the manager and company of the theatre, and in making the necessary arrangements for sending back my adopted orphan to his friends, with twenty pistoles. Finally, I directed the servants to say, if anybody enquired after me the next day, that I had gone out of town for some time; and after that, at five o'clock in the morning, I left my home in Paris never to return to it again.

By this time I had thoroughly recovered my tranquillity. I was as easy in my mind at leaving my house as I am now when I quit my cell to sing in the choir. Such already was the happy result of my perpetual masses, my general confession, and my three hours' interview with the vicar of Saint Sulpice.

Before taking leave of the world, I went to Versailles to say good-bye to my worthy patrons, Cardinal Fleury and the Duke de Gesvres. From them, I went to mass in the King's Chapel; and after that, I called on a lady of Versailles whom I had mortally offended, for the purpose of making my peace with her. She received me angrily enough. I told her I had not come to justify myself, but to ask her pardon. If she granted it, she would send me away happy. If she declined to be reconciled, Providence would probably be satisfied with my submission, but certainly not with her refusal. She felt the force of this argument; and we made it up on the spot.

I left Versailles immediately afterwards, without taking anything to eat; the act of humility which I had just performed being as good as a meal to me.

Towards evening, I entered the house of the Community of Saint Perpetua at Paris. I had ordered a little room to be furnished there for me, until the inventory of my worldly effects was completed, and until I could conclude my arrangements for entering a convent. On first installing myself, I began to feel hungry at last, and begged the Superior of the Community to give me for supper anything that remained from the dinner of the house. They had nothing but a little stewed carp, of which I eat with an excellent appetite. Marvellous to relate, although I had been able to keep nothing on my stomach for the past three months, although I had been dreadfully sick after a little rice soup on the evening before, the stewed carp of the sisterhood of Saint Perpetua, with some nuts afterwards for dessert, agreed with me charmingly, and I slept all through the night afterwards as peacefully as a child!

When the news of my retirement became public, it occasioned great talk in Paris. Various people assigned various reasons for the strange course that I had taken. Nobody, however, believed that I had quitted the world in the prime of my life (I was then thirty-one years old), never to return to it again. Meanwhile, my inventory was finished and my goods were sold. One of my friends sent a letter, entreating me to reconsider my determination. My mind was made up, and I wrote to say so. When my goods had been all sold, I left Paris to go and live incognito as a parlour-boarder in the Convent of the Ursuline nuns of Pondevaux. Here I wished to try the mode of life for a little while before I assumed the serious responsibility of taking the veil. I knew my own character—I remembered my early horror of total seclusion, and my inveterate dislike to the company of women only; and, moved by these considerations, I resolved, now that I had taken the first important step, to proceed in the future with caution.

The nuns of Pondevaux received me among them with great kindness. They gave me a large room, which I partitioned off into three small ones. I assisted at all the pious exercises of the place. Deceived by my fashionable appearance and my plump figure, the good nuns treated me as if I was a person of high distinction. This afflicted me, and I undeceived them. When they knew who I really was, they only behaved towards me with still greater kindness. I passed my time in reading and praying, and led the quietest, sweetest life it is possible to conceive.

After ten months' sojourn at Pondevaux, I went to Lyons, and entered (still as parlour-boarder only) the House of Anticaille, occupied by the nuns of the Order of Saint Mary. Here, I enjoyed the advantage of having for director of my conscience that holy man, Father Deveaux. He belonged to the Order of the Jesuits; and he was good enough, when I first asked him for advice, to suggest that I should get up at eleven o'clock at night to say my prayers, and should remain absorbed in devotion until midnight. In obedience to the directions of this saintly person, I kept myself awake as well as I could till eleven o'clock. I then got on my knees with great fervour, and I blush to confess it, immediately fell as fast asleep as a dormouse. This went on for several nights, when Father Deveaux finding that my midnight devotions were rather too much for me, was so obliging as to prescribe another species of pious exercise, in a letter which he wrote to me with his own hand. The holy father, after deeply regretting my inability to keep awake, informed me that he had a new act of penitence to suggest to me by the performance of which I might still hope to expiate my sins. He then, in the plainest terms, advised me to have recourse to the discipline of flagellation, every Friday, using the cat-o'-nine-tails on my bare shoulders for the length of time that it would take to repeat a Miserere. In conclusion, he informed me that the nuns of Anticaille would probably lend me the necessary instrument of flagellation; but, if they made any difficulty about it, he was benevolently ready to furnish me with a new and special cat-o'-nine-tails of his own making.

Never was woman more amazed or more angry than I, when I first read this letter. "What!" cried I to myself, "does this man seriously recommend me to lash my own shoulders? Just Heaven, what impertinence! And yet, is it not my duty to put up with it? Does not this apparent insolence proceed from the pen of a holy man? If he tells me to flog my wickedness out of me, is it not my bounden duty to lay on the scourge with all my might immediately? Sinner that I am! I am thinking remorsefully of my plump shoulders and the dimples on my back, when I ought to be thinking of nothing but the cat-o'-nine-tails and obedience to Father Deveaux?"

These reflections soon gave me the resolution which I had wanted at first. I was ashamed to ask the nuns for an instrument of flagellation; so I made one for myself of stout cord, pitilessly knotted at very short intervals. This done, I shut myself up while the nuns were at prayer, uncovered my shoulders, and rained such a shower of lashes on them, in the first fervour of my newly-awakened zeal, that I fairly flogged myself down on the ground, flat on my nose, before I had repeated more of the Miserere than the first two or three lines.

I burst out crying, shedding tears of spite against myself when I ought to have been shedding tears of devotional gratitude for the kindness of Father Deveaux. All through the night I never closed my eyes, and in the morning I found my poor shoulders (once so generally admired for their whiteness) striped with all the colours of the rainbow. The sight threw me into a passion, and I profanely said to myself while I was dressing, "The next time I see Father Deveaux, I will give my tongue full swing, and make the hair of that holy man stand on end with terror!" A few hours afterwards, he came to the convent, and all my resolution melted away at the sight of him. His imposing exterior had such an effect on me that I could only humbly entreat him to excuse me from indicting a second flagellation on myself. He smiled, benignantly, and granted my request with a saintly amiability. "Give me the cat-o'-nine-tails," he said, in conclusion, "and I will keep it for you till you ask me for it again. You are sure to ask for it again, dear child—to ask for it on your bended knees!"

Pious and prophetic man! Before many days had passed his words came true. If he had persisted severely in ordering me to flog myself, I might have opposed him for months together; but, as it was, who could resist the amiable indulgence he showed towards my weakness? The very next day after my interview, I began to feel ashamed of my own cowardice; and the day after that I went down on my knees, exactly as he had predicted, and said, "Father Deveaux, give me back my cat-o'-nine-tails." From that time I cheerfully underwent the discipline of flagellation, learning the regular method of practising it from the sisterhood, and feeling, in a spiritual point of view, immensely the better for it.

The nuns, finding that I cheerfully devoted myself to every act of self-sacrifice prescribed by the rules of their convent, wondered very much that I still hesitated about taking the veil. I begged them not to mention the subject to me till my mind was quite made up about it. They respected my wish, and said no more; but they lent me books to read which assisted in strengthening my wavering resolution. Among these books was the Life of Madame de Montmorenci, who, after the shocking death of her husband, entered the Order of St. Mary. The great example of this lady made me reflect seriously, and I communicated my thoughts, as a matter of course, to Father Deveaux. He assured me that the one last greatest sacrifice which remained for me to make was the sacrifice of my liberty. I had long known that this was my duty, and I now felt, for the first time, that I had courage and resolution enough boldly to face the idea of taking the veil.

While I was in this happy frame of mind, I happened to meet with the history of the famous Rancé, founder, or rather reformer, of the Order of La Trappe. I found a strange similarity between my own worldly errors and those of this illustrious penitent. The discovery had such an effect on me, that I spurned all idea of entering a convent where the rules were comparatively easy, as was the case at Anticaille, and determined, when I did take the veil, to enter an Order whose discipline was as severe as the discipline of La Trappe itself. Father Deveaux informed me that I should find exactly what I wanted among the Carmelite nuns; and, by his advice, I immediately put myself in communication with the Archbishop of Villeroi. I opened my heart to this worthy prelate, convinced him of my sincerity, and gained from him a promise that he would get me admitted among the Carmelite nuns of Lyons. One thing I begged of him at parting, which was, that he would tell the whole truth about my former life and about the profession that I had exercised in the world. I was resolved to deceive nobody, and to enter no convent under false pretences of any sort.

My wishes were scrupulously fulfilled; and the nuns were dreadfully frightened when they heard that I had been an actress at Paris. But the Archbishop promising to answer for me, and to take all their scruples on his own conscience, they consented to receive me. I could not trust myself to take formal leave of the nuns of Anticaille, who had been so kind to me, and towards whom I felt so gratefully. So I wrote my farewell to them after privately leaving their house, telling them frankly the motives which animated me, and asking their pardon for separating myself from them in secret.

On the fourteenth of October, seventeen hundred and twenty-four, I entered the Carmelite convent at Lyons, eighteen months after my flight from the world, and my abandonment of my profession—to adopt which, I may say, in my own defence, that I was first led through sheer poverty. At the age of seventeen years, and possessing (if I may credit report) remarkable personal charms, I was left perfectly destitute through the spendthrift habits of my father. I was easily persuaded to go on the stage, and soon tempted, with my youth and inexperience, to lead an irregular life. I do not wish to assert that dissipation necessarily follows the choice of the actress's profession, for I have known many estimable women on the stage. I, unhappily, was not one of the number. I confess it to my shame, and, as the chief of sinners, I am only the more grateful to the mercy of Heaven which accomplished my conversion.

When I entered the convent, I entreated the prioress to let me live in perfect obscurity, without corresponding with my friends, or even with my relations. She declined to grant this last request, thinking that my zeal was leading me too far. On the other hand, she complied with my wish to be employed at once, without the slightest preparatory indulgence or consideration, on any menial labour which the discipline of the convent might require from me. On the first day of my admission a broom was put into my hands. I was appointed also to wash up the dishes, to scour the saucepans, to draw water from a deep well, to carry each sister's pitcher to its proper place, and to scrub the tables in the refectory. From these occupations I got on in time to making rope shoes for the sisterhood, and to taking care of the great clock of the convent; this last employment requiring me to pull up three immensely heavy weights regularly every day. Seven years of my life passed in this hard work, and I can honestly say that I never murmured over it.

To return, however, to the period of my admission into the convent.

After three months of probation, I took the veil on the twentieth of January, seventeen hundred and twenty-five. The Archbishop did me the honour to preside at the ceremony; and, in spite of the rigour of the season, all Lyons poured into the church to see me take the vows. I was deeply affected; but I never faltered in my resolution. I pronounced the oaths with a firm voice, and with a tranquillity which astonished all the spectators,—a tranquillity which has never once failed me since that time.

Such is the story of my conversion. Providence sent me into the world with an excellent nature, with a true heart, with a remarkable susceptibility to the influence of estimable sentiments. My parents neglected my education, and left me in the world, destitute of everything but youth, beauty, and a lively temperament. I tried hard to be virtuous; I vowed, before I was out of my teens, and when I happened to be struck down by a serious illness, to leave the stage, and to keep my reputation unblemished, if anybody would only give me two hundred livres a year to live upon. Nobody came forward to help me, and I fell.

Heaven pardon the rich people of Paris who might have preserved my virtue at so small a cost! Heaven grant me courage to follow the better path into which its mercy has led me, and to persevere in a life of penitence and devotion to the end of my days!

So this singular confession ends. Besides the little vanities and levities which appear here and there on its surface, there is surely a strong undercurrent of sincerity and frankness which fit it to appeal in some degree to the sympathy as well as the curiosity of the reader. It is impossible to read the narrative without feeling that there must have been something really genuine and hearty in Mademoiselle Gautier's nature; and it is a gratifying proof of the honest integrity of her purpose to know that she persevered to the last in the life of humility and seclusion which her conscience had convinced her was the best life that she could lead. Persons who knew her in the Carmelite convent, report that she lived and died in it, preserving to the last, all the better part of the youthful liveliness of her character. She always received visitors with pleasure, always talked to them with surprising cheerfulness, always assisted the poor, and always willingly wrote letters to her former patrons in Paris to help the interests of her needy friends. Towards the end of her life, she was afflicted with blindness; but she was a trouble to no one in consequence of this affliction, for she continued, in spite of it, to clean her own cell, to make her own bed, and to cook her own food just as usual. One little characteristic vanity—harmless enough, surely?—remained with her to the last. She never forgot her own handsome face, which all Paris had admired in the by-gone time; and she contrived to get a dispensation from the Pope which allowed her to receive visitors in the convent parlour without a veil.

About Author

Early life

Collins was born at 11 New Cavendish Street, Marylebone, London, the son of a well-known Royal Academician landscape painter, William Collins and his wife, Harriet Geddes. Named after his father, he swiftly became known by his middle name, which honoured his godfather, David Wilkie. The family moved to Pond Street, Hampstead, in 1826. In 1828 Collins's brother Charles Allston Collins was born. Between 1829 and 1830, the Collins family moved twice, first to Hampstead Square and then to Porchester Terrace, Bayswater. Wilkie and Charles received their early education from their mother at home. The Collins family were deeply religious, and Collins's mother enforced strict church attendance on her sons, which Wilkie disliked.

In 1835, Collins began attending school at the Maida Vale academy. From 1836 to 1838, he lived with his parents in Italy and France, which made a great impression on him. He learned Italian while the family was in Italy and began learning French, in which he would eventually become fluent. From 1838 to 1840, he attended the Reverend Cole's private boarding school in Highbury, where he was bullied by a boy who would force Collins to tell him a story before allowing him to go to sleep. "It was this brute who first awakened in me, his poor little victim, a power of which but for him I might never have been aware.... When I left school I continued story telling for my own pleasure", Collins later said.

In 1840 the family moved to 85 Oxford Terrace, Bayswater. In late 1840, he left school and was apprenticed as a clerk to the firm of tea merchants Antrobus & Co, owned by a friend of Wilkie's father. He disliked his clerical work but remained employed by the company for more than five years. Collins's first story The Last Stage Coachman, was published in the Illuminated Magazine in August 1843. In 1844 he travelled to Paris with Charles Ward. That same year he wrote his first novel, Iolani, or Tahiti as It Was; a Romance, which was submitted to Chapman and Hall but rejected in 1845. The novel remained unpublished during his lifetime. Collins said of it:

"My youthful imagination ran riot among the noble savages, in scenes which caused the respectable British publisher to declare that it was impossible to put his name on the title page of such a novel." It was during the writing of this novel that Collins's father first learned that his assumptions that Wilkie would follow him in becoming a painter were mistaken.

William Collins had intended Wilkie for a clergyman and was disappointed in his son's lack of interest. In 1846 he instead entered Lincoln's Inn to study law, on the initiative of his father, who wanted him to have a steady income. Wilkie showed only a slight interest in law and spent most of his time with friends and on working on a second novel, Antonina, or the Fall of Rome. After his father's death in 1847, Collins produced his first published book, Memoirs of the Life of William Collins, Esq., R. A., published in 1848. The family moved to 38 Blandford Square soon afterwards, where they used their drawing room for amateur theatricals. In 1849, Collins exhibited a painting, "The Smugglers' Retreat", at the Royal Academy summer exhibition. Antonina was published by Richard Bentley in February 1850. Collins went on a walking tour of Cornwall with artist Henry Brandling in July and August 1850. He managed to complete his legal studies and be called to the bar in 1851. Though he never formally practised, he used his legal knowledge in many of his novels.

Early writing career

An instrumental event in his career was an introduction in March 1851 to Charles Dickens by a mutual friend, through the painter Augustus Egg. They became lifelong friends and collaborators. In May of that year, Collins acted with Dickens in Edward Bulwer-Lytton's play Not So Bad As We Seem. Among the audience were Queen Victoria and Prince Albert. Collins's story "A Terribly Strange Bed," his first contribution to Household Words, appeared in April, 1852. In May 1852 he went on tour with Dickens's company of amateur actors, again performing Not So Bad As We Seem, but with a more substantial role. Collins's novel Basil was published by Bentley in November. During the writing of Hide and Seek, in early 1853, Collins suffered what was probably his first attack of gout, which would plague him for the rest of his life. He was ill from April to early July. After that he stayed with Dickens in Boulogne from July to September 1853, then toured Switzerland and Italy with Dickens and Egg from October to December. Collins published Hide and Seek in June 1854.

During this period Collins extended the variety of his writing, publishing articles in George Henry Lewes's paper The Leader, short stories and essays for Bentley's Miscellany, dramatic criticism and the travel book Rambles Beyond Railways. His first play, The Lighthouse, was performed by Dickens's theatrical company at Tavistock House, in 1855. His first collection of short stories, After Dark, was published by Smith, Elder in February 1856. His novel A Rogue's Life was serialised in Household Words in March 1856. Around then, Collins began using laudanum regularly to treat his gout. He became addicted and struggled with that problem later in life.

Collins joined the staff of Household Words in October 1856. In 1856–57 he collaborated closely with Dickens on a play, The Frozen Deep, first performed in Tavistock. Collins's novel The Dead Secret was serialised in Household Words from January to June 1857 and published in volume form by Bradbury and Evans. Collins's play The Lighthouse was performed at the Olympic Theatre in August. The Lazy Tour of Two Idle Apprentices, based on Dickens's and Collins's walking tour in the north of England, was serialised in Household Words in October 1857. In 1858 he collaborated with Dickens and other writers on the story "A House to Let".

1860s

According to biographer Melisa Klimaszewski, "The novels Collins published in the 1860s are the best and most enduring of his career. The Woman in White, No Name, Armadale, and The Moonstone, written in less than a decade, show Collins not just as a master of his craft, but as an innovater and provocateur. These four works, which secured him an international reputation, and sold in large numbers, ensured his financial stability, and allowed him to support many others".

The Woman in White was serialised in All the Year Round from November 1859 to August 1860 and was a great success. The novel was published in book form soon after serial publication ended, and it reached an eighth edition by November 1860. His increased stature as a writer made Collins resign his position with All the Year Round in 1862 to focus on novel writing. During the planning of his next novel, No Name, he continued to suffer from gout, and it now especially affected his eyes. Serial publication of No Name began in early 1862 and finished in 1863. By this time the laudanum he was taking for his continual gout became a serious problem.

At the beginning of 1863, he travelled to German spas and Italy for his health, with Caroline Graves. In 1864, he began work on his novel Armadale, travelling in August to do research for it. It was published serially in The Cornhill Magazine in 1864–66. His play No Thoroughfare, co-written with Dickens, was published as the 1867 Christmas number of All the Year Round and dramatised at the Adelphi Theatre on 26 December. It enjoyed a run of 200 nights before being taken on tour.

Collins's search for background information for Armadale took him to the Norfolk Broads and the small village of Winterton-on-Sea. His novel The Moonstone was serialised in All the Year Round from January to August 1868. His mother, Harriet Collins, died that year.

Later years

In 1870, his novel Man and Wife was published. This year also saw the death of Charles Dickens, which caused him great sadness. He said of their early days together, "We saw each other every day, and were as fond of each other as men could be."

The Woman in White was dramatised and produced at the Olympic Theatre in October 1871.

Collins's novel Poor Miss Finch was serialised in Cassell's Magazine from October to March 1872. His short novel Miss or Mrs? was published in the 1872 Christmas number of the Graphic. His novel The New Magdalen was serialised from October 1872 to July 1873. His younger brother, Charles Allston Collins, died later in 1873. Charles had married Dickens's younger daughter, Kate.

In 1873–74, Collins toured the United States and Canada, giving readings of his work. The American writers he met included Oliver Wendell Holmes, Sr., and Mark Twain, and he began a friendship with the photographer Napoleon Sarony, who took several portraits of him.

His novel The Law and the Lady, serialised in the Graphic from September to March 1875, was followed by a short novel, The Haunted Hotel, which was serialised from June to November 1878. His later novels include Jezebel's Daughter (1880), The Black Robe (1881), Heart and Science (1883) and The Evil Genius (1886). In 1884, Collins was elected Vice-President of the Society of Authors, which had been founded by his friend and fellow novelist Walter Besant.

The inconsistent quality of Collins's dramatic and fictional works in the last decade of his life was accompanied by a general decline in his health, including diminished eyesight. He was often unable to leave home and had difficulty writing. During these last years, he focused on mentoring younger writers, including the novelist Hall Caine, and helped to protect other writers from copyright infringement of their works. His writing became a way for him to fight his illness without allowing it to keep him bedridden. His step-daughter Harriet also served as an amanuensis for several years. His last novel, Blind Love, was finished posthumously by Walter Besant.

Death

Collins died at 82 Wimpole Street, following a paralytic stroke. He is buried in Kensal Green Cemetery, West London. His headstone describes him as the author of The Woman in White. Caroline Graves died in 1895 and was buried with Collins. Martha Rudd died in 1919.

Personal life

In 1858 Collins began living with Caroline Graves and her daughter Harriet. Caroline came from a humble family, having married young, had a child, and been widowed. Collins lived close to the small shop kept by Caroline, and the two may have met in the neighborhood in the mid–1850s. He treated Harriet, whom he called Carrie, as his own daughter, and helped to provide for her education. Excepting one short separation, they lived together for the rest of Collins's life. Collins disliked the institution of marriage, but remained dedicated to Caroline and Harriet, considering them to be his family. Caroline had wanted to marry Collins. She left him while he wrote The Moonstone and was suffering an attack of acute gout. She then married a younger man named Joseph Clow, but returned to Collins after two years.

In 1868, Collins met Martha Rudd in Winterton-on-Sea in Norfolk, and the two began a liaison. She was 19 years old and from a large, poor family. She moved to London to be closer to him a few years later. Their daughter Marian was born in 1869, their second daughter, Harriet Constance, in 1871 and their son, William Charles, in 1874. When he was with Martha he assumed the name William Dawson, and she and their children used the last name of Dawson themselves.

For the last 20 years of his life Collins divided his time between Caroline, who lived with him at his home in Gloucester Place, and Martha who was nearby.

Like his friend Charles Dickens, Collins was a professing Christian.

Works

Collins's works were classified at the time as "sensation novels", a genre seen nowadays as the precursor to detective and suspense fiction. He also wrote penetratingly on the plight of women and on the social and domestic issues of his time. For example, his 1854 Hide and Seek contained one of the first portrayals of a deaf character in English literature. As did many writers of his time, Collins published most of his novels as serials in magazines such as Dickens's All the Year Round and was known as a master of the form, creating just the right degree of suspense to keep his audience reading from week to week. Sales of All The Year Round increased when The Woman in White followed A Tale of Two Cities.

Collins enjoyed ten years of great success following publication of The Woman in White in 1859. His next novel, No Name combined social commentary – the absurdity of the law as it applied to children of unmarried parents (see Illegitimacy in fiction) – with a densely plotted revenge thriller.

Armadale, the first and only of Collins's major novels of the 1860s to be serialised in a magazine other than All the Year Round, provoked strong criticism, generally centred upon its transgressive villainess Lydia Gwilt, and provoked in part by Collins's typically confrontational preface. The novel was simultaneously a financial coup for its author and a comparative commercial failure: the sum paid by Cornhill for the serialisation rights was exceptional, eclipsing by a substantial margin the prices paid for the vast majority of similar novels, yet the novel failed to recoup its publisher's investment. The Moonstone, published in 1868, and the last novel of what is generally regarded as the most successful decade of its author's career, was, despite a somewhat cool reception from both Dickens and the critics, a significant return to form and reestablished the market value of an author whose success on the competitive Victorian literary market had been gradually waning in the wake of his first perceived masterpiece. Viewed by many to represent the advent of the detective story within the tradition of the English novel, The Moonstone remains one of Collins's most critically acclaimed productions, identified by T. S. Eliot as "the first, the longest, and the best of modern English detective novels... in a genre invented by Collins and not by Poe," and Dorothy L. Sayers referred to it as "probably the very finest detective story ever written".

After The Moonstone, Collins's novels contained fewer thriller elements and more social commentary. The subject matter continued to be sensational, but his popularity declined. The poet Algernon Charles Swinburne commented: "What brought good Wilkie's genius nigh perdition? / Some demon whispered—'Wilkie! have a mission.'"

Factors most often cited have been the death of Dickens in 1870, and with it the loss of his literary mentoring, Collins's increased dependence upon laudanum, and his penchant for using his fiction to rail against social injustices. His novels and novellas of the 1870s and 1880s are generally regarded as inferior to his previous productions and receive comparatively little critical attention today[when?].

The Woman in White and The Moonstone share an unusual narrative structure, somewhat resembling an epistolary novel, in which different portions of the book have different narrators, each with a distinct narrative voice. Armadale has this to a lesser extent through the correspondence between some characters. (Source: Wikipedia)

CPSIA information can be obtained
at www.ICGtesting.com
Printed in the USA
BVHW071247240719
554234BV00010B/1148/P